Save Your Acorns

How the Bears Saved the Monkeys

ROBERT GARDNER

Illustrated by Marina Veselinovic

LIONCREST
PUBLISHING

SAVE YOUR ACORNS

How the Bears Saved the Monkeys

ISBN 978-1-61961-417-8

This book belongs to:

....

On a warm autumn day, Oliver and Amelia were arguing.

"They're my acorns!" shouted Amelia.

"I helped collect them, so I should get to eat half of them!" said Oliver.

"Children!" said their wise old grandpa. "Neither of you should be eating all those acorns."

"Neither of us?" Amelia cried.

"Why not?" asked Oliver.

"Let me read you a story about the
bears and the monkeys," Grandpa said.

One summer, many years ago, the monkeys had the best banana harvest in years.

The monkeys had the time of their lives! They all ate dozens of bananas.

They had banana parties.

They even wasted the bananas by throwing them at each other!

But one day the weather changed.
No rain fell and the bananas
dried-up into nothing.

All the banana parties stopped. All the banana throwing stopped. Worst of all, eating bananas stopped. The monkeys grew extremely hungry.

Every day was worse than the one before it! Their tummies rumbled with hunger!

Luckily for the monkeys, their good friends the bears came to their rescue!

Rather than eating all their berries, the wise bears had saved some of their berries for the winter.

Every day they would eat enough to be full, and put the rest of their berries aside.

When the bears woke up from their winter sleep and saw how hungry the monkeys had grown, they knew they had to help.

They got together and agreed to share their saved berries with the monkeys.

From that year on, the monkeys knew not to waste their bananas by playing games and having parties.

Now the monkeys would save two out of every ten bananas for when the weather changed. They still had enough bananas to eat and feel full.

"Wow, those monkeys sure were silly," said Oliver.

"I'd never want to run out of food and be hungry like the monkeys," said Amelia.

Grandpa smiled. "That's why every time we find ten acorns, the first thing we do is save two of them, just in case."

"That way, when we aren't so lucky,
we'll always have extra acorns."

"I haven't told you the best part," said Grandpa. "When you save your acorns, they don't just sit there and wait for you. They grow into trees, and the trees give you more and more acorns."

"The longer you wait, the more acorns you have," Grandpa said.

"I can't wait to save our acorns!" said Oliver.

"Maybe one day, we'll even have enough acorns to help our friends, just like the bears did!" exclaimed Amelia.

The End

NOTE TO PARENTS AND TEACHERS

In today's world of instant gratification, the idea of saving for the future is more important than ever. It is natural for children to want things right away. This story shows them that wasting things—such as money—can have serious consequences. As Amelia and Oliver learn in the story, if you work hard and save, you can make sure that you will have a supply of acorns when you need it.

Another important theme in the story is how the amount of acorns can grow through saving. When acorns are saved, Amelia and Oliver learn, they grow into trees that produce more acorns. Saving money in the bank works the same way. The longer money is saved, the more the amount grows because of the interest earned.

The story also stresses the importance of giving. The bears give generously of their berries to the monkeys. Later in the story, Amelia hopes to share some of her acorns with her friends. Children learn, through this example, that charity is an important part of becoming good citizens.

After you read the story to your children, ask them the following questions:

- *What did you learn when the monkeys wasted their bananas? Have you ever wasted anything?*

- *What did you learn when the bears shared their berries? Have you ever shared with a friend who needed something?*

- *The acorns the squirrels save are similar to money you may earn or get for an allowance or as a gift. Do you save your money so that you can get something special?*

Visit www.saveyouracorns.com
for activities, games and fun.

 Follow us at @saveyouracorns

 facebook.com/SaveYourAcorns

 www.fairlife.org.uk